GW00673762

THE BEST OF
YIRUMA

 VOLONTÈ&CO

Yiruma's musical journey began at age five, when a fascination with the piano grew into a love for music and composition. He moved to England at the age of 10 to join the prestigious Purcell School of Music, then enrolled in London University of King's College to learn from the highly esteemed Sir Harrison Birtwistle.

Yiruma's first album, Love Scene, came out in 2001, and demonstrated his skill in combining friendly, approachable melodies with a polished performance. That same year, he wrote the follow-up collection, First Love, which included the iconic No.1 hit River Flows in You. In 2002, Yiruma performed at the prestigious Marché International du Disque et de l'Edition Musicale in Cannes, the first Korean musician to do so.

2003 saw the release of Yiruma's third album, titled From the Yellow Room, and a host of sell-out shows in South Korea. Yiruma's success continued to flourish internationally as well. In 2012, he made an appearance on the German TV show Wilkommen Bei Carmen Nebel, and in the following years, he held sold-out concerts in a myriad of countries and popular venues, such as the New York Carnegie Hall, Lincoln Center and Sydney Opera House.

The advent of streaming brought new audiences, with the pianist-composer earning over two billion streams through various platforms and more than 500 million views on YouTube. With new opportunities presented by online platforms, Yiruma's 10th Anniversary compilation album The Best: Reminiscent shot to number one in the US billboard charts and has dominated the charts for some time. This marked yet another milestone in album sales, becoming the second platinum award to add to his already amassed pair of gold awards.

Yiruma continues to find inspiration in people around him, and hopes his music can heal, inspire, and remind the audience of love and hope. With each piece, Yiruma prays that he can show God's love by intertwining his aspirations with music that connects with people all around the world.

YIRUMA

I hope my music finds its way into your hands whenever you feel

happiness, heaviness, or need light in your darkest times.

This was what I wished for, and this wish could come true through you.

I sincerely hope that someday the music remains a part of your memory.

Yiruma

Poem+

이루마 Yiruma

2

YIRUMA

River Flows in You

이루마 Yiruma

Chaconne

이루마 Yiruma

Kiss The Rain

이루마 Yiruma

May Be

이루마 Yiruma

Do You?

이루마 Yiruma

4

6

Passing By

이루마 Yiruma

Fotografia

이루마 Yiruma

4

Scenery through the window

이루마 Yiruma

YIRUMA

Indigo

이루마 Yiruma

Yiruma

flower

이루마 Yiruma

Sky

이루마 Yiruma

2

YIRUMA

Wait There

이루마 Yiruma

Love Me

이루마 Yiruma

Infinia

이루마 Yiruma

Preludio al Vento

이루마 Yiruma

Fairy Tale

이루마 Yiruma

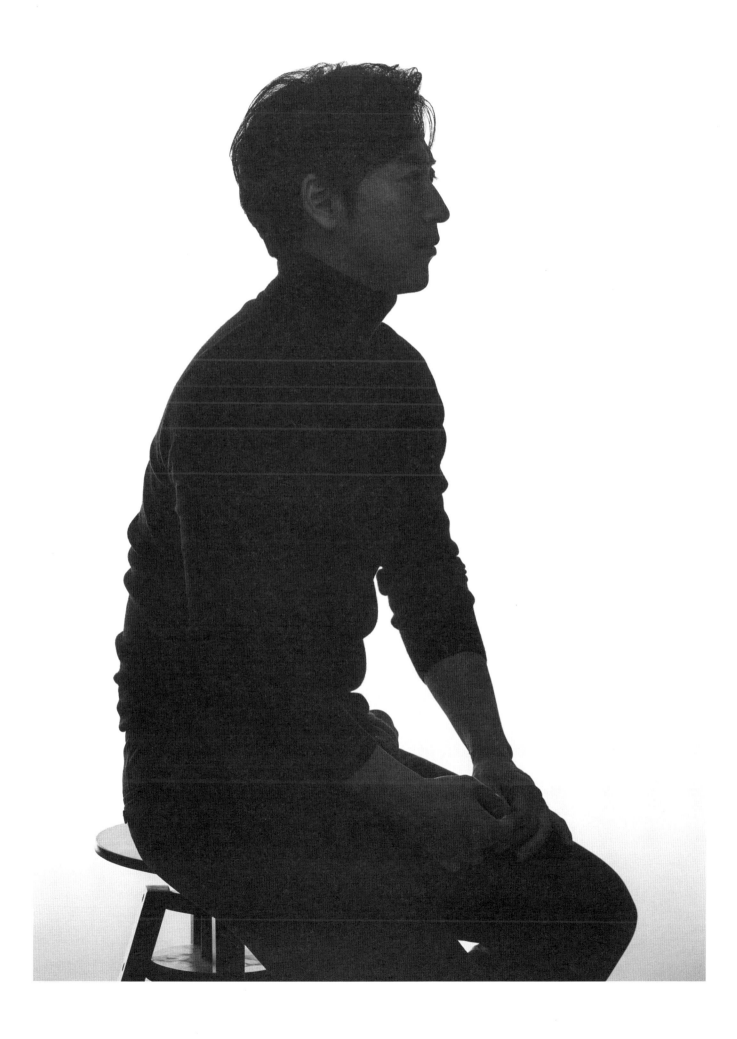

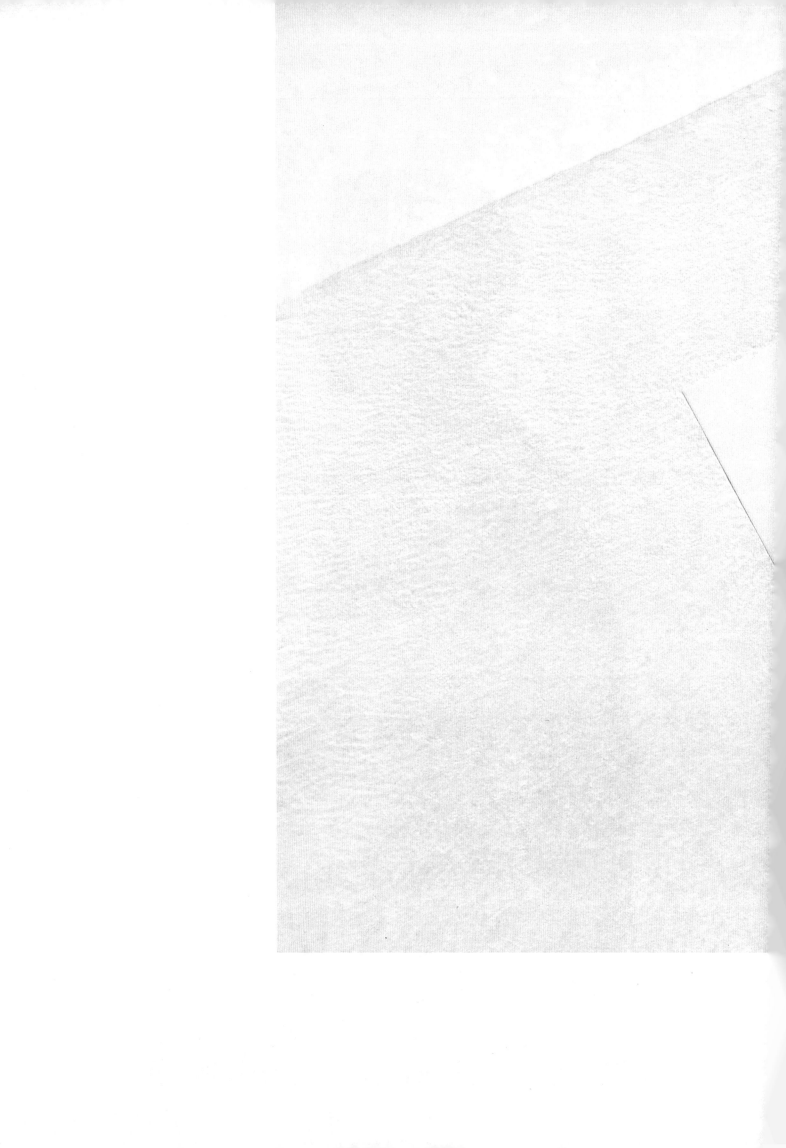

THE BEST OF
YIRUMA

© 2020 YIRUMA & MAPIA Music and Publishing Co.,Ltd. All songs are written & scored by YIRUMA.
Under Exclusive license to Volonté & Co Srl – Milan in Europe. Designed by Onsil Studio.
Manufactured & Distributed by Volonté & Co Srl. All Rights Reserved.
Unauthorized duplication is a violation of applicable laws.

THE BEST OF
YIRUMA

© 2020 YIRUMA & MAPIA Music and Publishing Co.,Ltd. All songs are written & scored by YIRUMA.
Under Exclusive license to Volonté & Co Srl – Milan in Europe. Designed by Onsil Studio.
Manufactured & Distributed by Volonté & Co Srl. All Rights Reserved.
Unauthorized duplication is a violation of applicable laws.